PreScripts

CURSIVE PASSAGES AND ILLUMINATIONS

AMERICAN DOCUMENTS

PreScripts Cursive Passages and Illuminations:
American Documents

Created by Courtney Sanford and Jennifer Greenholt
Layout by Kelly Digges

© 2013 by Classical Conversations® MultiMedia
All rights reserved.

Scripture verses marked KJV are from the King James Version of the Bible. Those marked NIV are taken from the Holy Bible, New International Version®. NIV®. Copyright © 1973, 1978, 1984 by International Bible Society. Used by permission of Zondervan. All rights reserved.

Published in the U.S.A. by Classical Conversations, Inc.
P.O. Box 909
West End, NC 27376

ISBN: 978-0-9884965-3-8

For ordering information, visit www.ClassicalConversationsBooks.com.
Printed in the United States of America

PreScripts Cursive Passages and Illuminations: American Documents

The word "prescript" comes from the Latin words *prae* (meaning "before" or "in front of") plus *scribere* ("to write"). The PreScripts series from Classical Conversations MultiMedia is designed to precede—to come before—writing. Just as we learn to speak by mimicking our parents' words, we can learn to write well by copying the words that others have written. Even though coloring, drawing, tracing, and copying are simple tasks from an adult perspective, imitation is at the heart of a classical education. Rather than resorting to mindless busywork that isolates handwriting from the rest of education, the PreScripts series is designed to complement the world of knowledge students inhabit as they mature.

How to Use This Book

Each book in the PreScripts series combines a functional design with excellent content. The goal of *PreScripts Cursive Passages and Illuminations* is to refine the basics of cursive writing through practice with longer passages of writing. As your students gain muscle strength and coordination, they will be able to move from writing that is functional to writing that is worthy of being called an art. For this reason, this book in the PreScripts series can be used as either a consumable or a non-consumable resource. Students who still have difficulty with the cursive letters can trace over the writing in the book and practice drawing the letter illuminations in the space provided, while those who are ready for a challenge can copy the passages in a separate notebook or on blank paper.

Our job as classical educators is to teach students to make the effort to be neat but even more, it is to encourage them to aim higher by teaching them to write beautifully. Many schools no longer teach cursive writing, claiming that it is too difficult to master. Teaching a child to write in cursive does require diligence and patience, but it has a number of compelling benefits. Research suggests that cursive writing more effectively develops manual skill and dexterity. Cursive may also aid students struggling with dyslexia or dysgraphia because 1) capital and lowercase letters are distinct; 2) each word is one fluid movement, so the child's rhythm is not disrupted by frequent pauses; and 3) letters like "b" and "d" are more difficult to reverse.

When children are learning to write, what they study matters as much as how they study it. Parents are more likely to give up on cursive when the content seems frivolous, so Classical Conversations is pleased to offer cursive writing books that give the student plenty of practice using rich, meaningful content. With PreScripts cursive writing books, your student can become a confident writer while learning or reviewing important subject matter, such as history sentences, passages of literature, and proverbs.

In this book, we focus on passages taken from great historical American documents and speeches ranging from Christopher Columbus's "Apologia" and the Mayflower Compact to the Marshall Plan and John F. Kennedy's Inaugural Address. (If you wish to study these documents in full, an excellent companion book is *Words Aptly Spoken: American Documents*, also by Classical Conversations MultiMedia.) Each passage gives your student an example of admirable rhetorical skill that is grounded in the context of important events from the history of the United States.

To provide variety for your student and to enhance the fine motor skills necessary for writing, drawing lessons accompany the copy work. This book focuses on illumination, an art form dating back to the classical and medieval periods, when manuscripts were written by hand and each one was treated as a valuable work of art. The word "illumination" comes from the Latin verb *illuminare*, which means, "to light up." In the most luxurious illuminated manuscripts, an artist would take sheets of real gold or silver that had been beaten into extremely thin layers called "leaves," and he would incorporate the precious metals into his drawings and lettering. When light hit the gilded page, the manuscript would seem to shine with its own matching light.

In addition to the cost of materials, illuminated manuscripts required an immense investment of time and effort. A single book could take as few as two years or as many as fifty to produce. To give you a sense of an illuminated book's resulting value, one buyer in 1453 is said to have sold a small estate to pay for a single copy of Livy's *History of Rome*. King Louis XI of France not only had to pay a deposit in silver but he also had to give his personal guarantee and that of another nobleman before he was allowed to borrow a book from the Faculty of Medicine in Paris. Imagine if today's libraries were so stringent!

Although many artists were associated with monasteries, others were members of the nobility or independent craftsmen, both male and female. Their illuminations included ornate borders, miniature drawings, elaborate initial letters, and full-page images. They used lines, curves, dots, flowers, leaves, branches, animals, and people in their art—in short, all the elements of drawing. This book will focus on initial letters, but you should encourage your student to experiment with his own artwork, giving a personal touch to each passage he copies.

Although variety is important, the key to mastering cursive is to practice every day. For best results, set aside a specific time each day for cursive practice. You choose the pace appropriate for your child. You can assign one page a day to a beginning student or assign two to four pages a day to an older or more experienced student. A student who struggles with writing might even do half a page a day until his or her fine motor skills become stronger, working up to a page or two a day. The pace is completely up to the parent.

If you choose to do one page a day, there are enough pages for a complete school year, working on approximately four or five pages a week. If you participate in a Classical Conversations community, you can do four pages a week while your community meets, and five pages a week the rest of the school year. Older students might do two pages a day and complete two books a year. If you would like your child to memorize the passages in this book, you can read through them weekly to review or have your student do the same book twice.

The Journey in Perspective

The key to good writing is daily practice. The key to a heart that seeks truth, beauty, and goodness is providing quality content to copy. We hope you will find both in *Prescripts Cursive Passages and Illuminations*.

The medieval scribes and artists who practiced illumination often did so in the service of the Church. As such, they believed that words, particularly sacred texts, were worthy of honor and respect, and they used their art to exalt the words they copied. Likewise, the goal of the PreScripts series is for your students to master the skills of copying and writing in the context of a biblical worldview, building on a second meaning of the word "prescript." A prescript can also mean a command, rule, or moral guideline. The Bible instructs parents to remember the commandments of God and teach them to their families.

Deuteronomy 6:6–9 reads, "And these words which I command you today shall be in your heart. You shall teach them diligently to your children, and shall talk of them when you sit in your house, when you walk by the way, when you lie down, and when you rise up. You shall bind them as a sign on your hand, and they shall be as frontlets between your eyes. You shall write them on the doorposts of your house and on your gates." As this Scripture reminds us, writing, drawing, memorizing, and reciting are all forms of worship that we model for our students.

Let's get started!

For more information about the practice of illumination, the following copyright-free resources are available in e-book form.

- Bradley, John William. *Illuminated Manuscripts*. Little Books on Art. Ed. Cyril Davenport. Chicago: A.C. McClurg & Co., 1909.

- Middleton, John Henry. *Illuminated Manuscripts in Classical and Mediaeval Times*. London: C.J. Clay & Sons, 1892.

- Quaile, Edward. *Illuminated Manuscripts: Their Origin, History, and Characteristics*. Liverpool, UK: H. Young & Sons, 1897.

If you and your student wish to undertake a more detailed, contemporary study of illumination, you might consider purchasing a book such as Michelle Brown's *Understanding Illuminated Manuscripts: A Guide to Technical Terms* (Los Angeles: Getty Publications, 1994).

he art of sailing is favorable

for anyone who wants to

pursue knowledge of this world's secrets...

I found our Lord very well disposed toward

this desire, and he gave me the spirit for

it. He prospered me in seamanship and

supplied me with the necessary tools

of astronomy, as well as geometry and

arithmetic and ingenuity of manual skill

to draw spherical maps which show cities,

rivers and mountains, islands and ports—

everything in its proper place.

Practice your own illuminated letter here.

W ho can desire more content,

that hath small means;

or but only his merit to

advance his fortune, than to tread, and

plant that ground he hath purchased by

the hazard of his life? If he have but the

taste of virtue, and magnanimity, what to

such a mind can be more pleasant, than

planting and building a foundation for

his posterity, got from the rude earth,

by God's blessing and his own industry,

without prejudice to any?

Practice your own illuminated letter here.

Having undertaken for the Glory of God, and Advancement of the Christian Faith, and the Honor of our King and Country, a Voyage to plant the first colony in the northern Parts of Virginia; Do by these Presents,) solemnly and mutually in the Presence of God and one another, covenant and combine ourselves together into a civil Body Politick, for our better Ordering and Preservation, and Furtherance of the Ends aforesaid.

Practice your own illuminated letter here.

 eing thus arrived in a good

harbor, and brought safe

to land, they fell upon their knees and

blessed the God of Heaven who had brought

them over the vast and furious ocean, and

delivered them from all the perils and

miseries thereof, again to set their feet on

the firm and stable earth, their proper

element.

Practice your own illuminated letter here.

For two years together after the beginning of the colony, whereof he was now governor, the poor people had a great experiment of "man's not living by bread alone;" for when they were left all together without one morsel of bread for many months, one after another, still the good Providence of God relieved them, and supplied them, and this for the most part out of the sea.

Practice your own illuminated letter here.

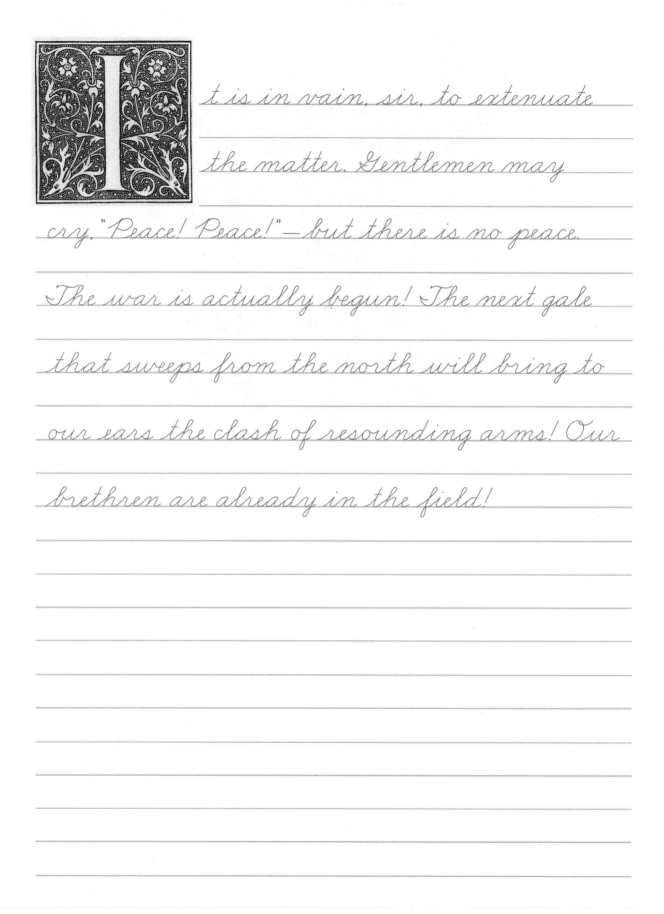

It is in vain, sir, to extenuate the matter. Gentlemen may cry, "Peace! Peace!"—but there is no peace. The war is actually begun! The next gale that sweeps from the north will bring to our ears the clash of resounding arms! Our brethren are already in the field!

Practice your own illuminated letter here.

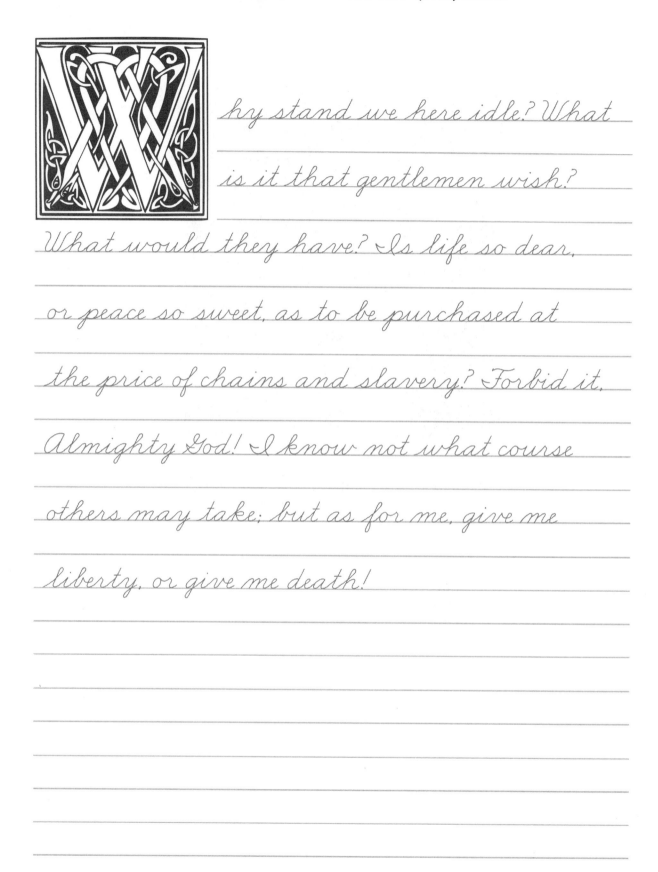

hy stand we here idle? What

is it that gentlemen wish?

What would they have? Is life so dear,

or peace so sweet, as to be purchased at

the price of chains and slavery? Forbid it,

Almighty God! I know not what course

others may take; but as for me, give me

liberty, or give me death!

Practice your own illuminated letter here.

These are the times that try men's souls. The summer soldier and the sunshine patriot will, in this crisis, shrink from the service of their country; but he that stands by it now, deserves the love and thanks of man and woman. Tyranny, like hell, is not easily conquered; yet we have this consolation with us, that the harder the conflict, the more glorious the triumph.

Practice your own illuminated letter here.

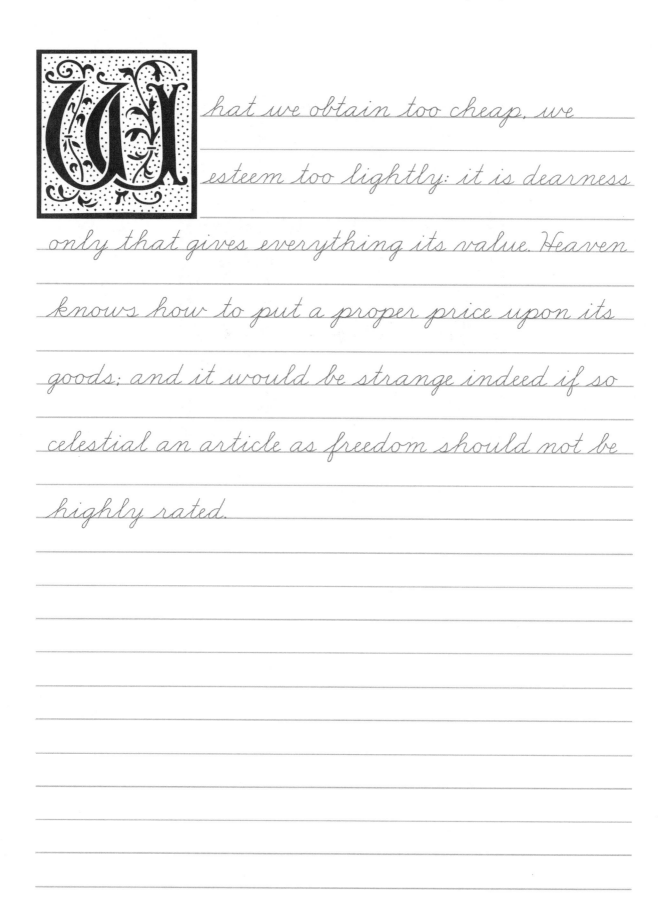

What we obtain too cheap, we esteem too lightly: it is dearness only that gives everything its value. Heaven knows how to put a proper price upon its goods: and it would be strange indeed if so celestial an article as freedom should not be highly rated.

Practice your own illuminated letter here.

When in the Course of human

events it becomes necessary for one

people to dissolve the political bands which

have connected them with another and to

assume among the powers of the earth, the

separate and equal station to which the

Laws of Nature and of Nature's God entitle

them, a decent respect to the opinions

of mankind requires that they should

declare the causes which impel them to the

separation.

Practice your own illuminated letter here.

We hold these truths to be self-evident, that all men are created equal, that they are endowed by their Creator with certain unalienable Rights, that among these are Life, Liberty and the pursuit of Happiness. —That to secure these rights, Governments are instituted among Men, deriving their just powers from the consent of the governed. —

Practice your own illuminated letter here.

That whenever any Form of Government becomes destructive of these ends, it is the Right of the People to alter or to abolish it, and to institute new Government, laying its foundation on such principles and organizing its power in such form, as to them shall seem most likely to effect their Safety and Happiness.

Practice your own illuminated letter here.

Each state retains its sovereignty,

freedom, and independence,

and every Power, Jurisdiction, and right,

which is not by this confederation expressly

delegated to the United States, in Congress

assembled.

Practice your own illuminated letter here.

The said states hereby severally enter into a firm league of friendship with each other, for their common defence, the security of their Liberties, and their mutual and general welfare, binding themselves to assist each other, against all force offered to, or attacks made upon them, or any of them, on account of religion, sovereignty, trade, or any other pretence whatever.

Practice your own illuminated letter here.

Religion, morality, and knowledge, being necessary to good government and the happiness of mankind, schools and the means of education shall forever be encouraged.

Practice your own illuminated letter here.

The utmost good faith shall always be observed towards the Indians; their lands and property shall never be taken from them without their consent; and, in their property, rights, and liberty, they shall never be invaded or disturbed, unless in just and lawful wars authorized by Congress; but laws founded in justice and humanity, shall from time to time be made for preventing wrongs being done to them, and for preserving peace and friendship with them.

Practice your own illuminated letter here.

How is it possible that a government half supplied and always necessitous, can fulfill the purposes of its institution, can provide for the security, advance the prosperity, or support the reputation of the commonwealth? How can it ever possess either energy or stability, dignity or credit, confidence at home or respectability abroad?

Practice your own illuminated letter here.

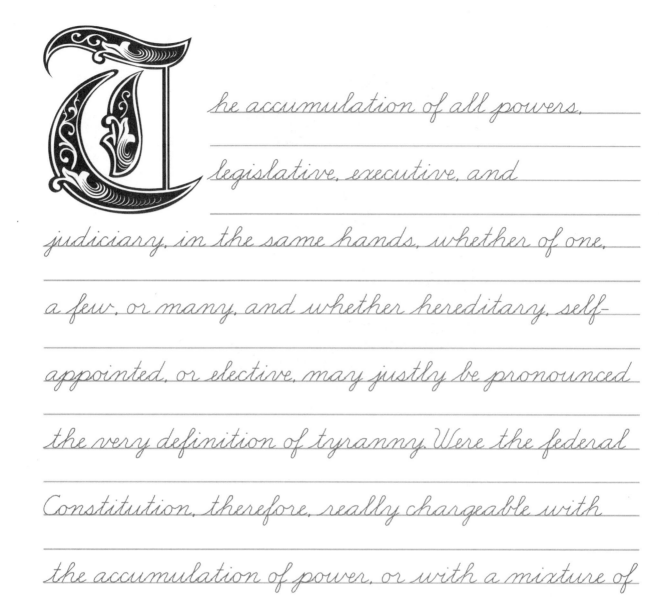

The accumulation of all powers, legislative, executive, and judiciary, in the same hands, whether of one, a few, or many, and whether hereditary, self-appointed, or elective, may justly be pronounced the very definition of tyranny. Were the federal Constitution, therefore, really chargeable with the accumulation of power, or with a mixture of powers, having a dangerous tendency to such an accumulation, no further arguments would be necessary to inspire a universal reprobation of the system.

Practice your own illuminated letter here.

e the People of the United States,
in Order to form a more perfect
Union, establish Justice, insure domestic
Tranquility, provide for the common defence,
promote the general Welfare, and secure the
Blessings of Liberty to ourselves and our
Posterity, do ordain and establish this
Constitution for the United States of America.

Practice your own illuminated letter here.

Before he enter on the Execution of his Office, he shall take the following Oath or Affirmation:—"I do solemnly swear (or affirm) that I will faithfully execute the Office of President of the United States, and will to the best of my Ability, preserve, protect and defend the Constitution of the United States."

Practice your own illuminated letter here.

There is no truth more thoroughly established, than that there exists in the economy and course of nature, an indissoluble union between virtue and happiness, between duty and advantage, between the genuine maxims of an honest and magnanimous policy, and the solid rewards of public prosperity and felicity.

Practice your own illuminated letter here.

ince the general civilization of mankind I believe there are more instances of the abridgment of the freedom of the people by gradual and silent encroachments of those in power than by violent and sudden usurpations; but, on a candid examination of history, we shall find that turbulence, violence, and abuse of power, by the majority trampling on the rights of the minority, have produced factions and commotions which, in republics, have more frequently than any other cause, produced despotism.

Practice your own illuminated letter here.

Accordingly he signed the manumission that day, so that, before night, I who had been a slave in the morning, trembling at the will of another, now became my own master and completely free. I thought this was the happiest day I had ever experienced; and my joy was still heightened by the blessings and prayers of the sable race, particularly the aged, to whom my heart had ever been attached with reverence.

Practice your own illuminated letter here.

Congress shall make no law

respecting an establishment

of religion, or prohibiting the free exercise

thereof; or abridging the freedom of speech,

or of the press; or the right of the people

peaceably to assemble, and to petition the

Government for a redress of grievances.

Practice your own illuminated letter here.

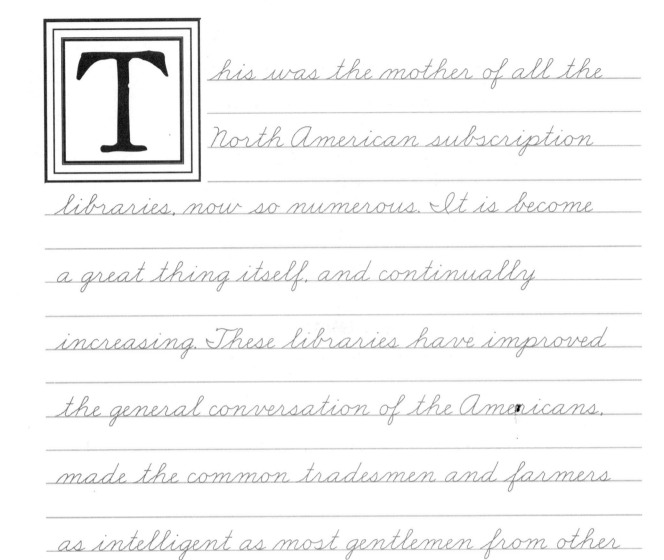

This was the mother of all the North American subscription libraries, now so numerous. It is become a great thing itself, and continually increasing. These libraries have improved the general conversation of the Americans, made the common tradesmen and farmers as intelligent as most gentlemen from other countries, and perhaps have contributed in some degree to the stand so generally made throughout the colonies in defense of their privileges.

Practice your own illuminated letter here.

he name of American, which belongs to you in your national capacity, must always exalt the just pride of patriotism more than any appellation derived from local discriminations. With slight shades of difference, you have the same religion, manners, habits, and political principles. You have in a common cause fought and triumphed together; the independence and liberty you possess are the work of joint counsels, and joint efforts of common dangers, sufferings, and successes.

Practice your own illuminated letter here.

Observe good faith and justice toward all nations; cultivate peace and harmony with all. Religion and morality enjoin this conduct; and can it be, that good policy does not equally enjoin it? It will be worthy of a free, enlightened, and at no distant period, a great nation, to give to mankind the magnanimous and too novel example of a people always guided by an exalted justice and benevolence.

Practice your own illuminated letter here.

And be it further enacted, That

in all that territory ceded by

France to the United States, under the

name of Louisiana, which lies north of

thirty-six degrees and thirty minutes north

latitude, not included within the limits of

the state, contemplated by this act, slavery

and involuntary servitude, otherwise than

in the punishment of crimes, whereof the

parties shall have been duly convicted,

shall be, and is hereby, forever prohibited:

Practice your own illuminated letter here.

Provided always, That any person escaping into the same, from whom labour or service is lawfully claimed, in any state or territory of the United States, such fugitive may be lawfully reclaimed and conveyed to the person claiming his or her labour or service as aforesaid.

Practice your own illuminated letter here.

The citizens of the United States cherish sentiments the most friendly, in favor of the liberty and happiness of their fellow men on that side of the Atlantic. In the wars of the European powers, in matters relating to themselves, we have never taken any part, nor does it comport with our policy to do so. It is only when our rights are invaded, or seriously menaced, that we resent injuries, or make preparation for our defence.

Practice your own illuminated letter here.

Now, in view of this entire disfranchisement of one-half the people of this country, their social and religious degradation—in view of the unjust laws above mentioned, and because women do feel themselves aggrieved, oppressed, and fraudulently deprived of their most sacred rights, we insist that they have immediate admission to all the rights and privileges which belong to them as citizens of the United States.

Practice your own illuminated letter here.

s we were walking the other day, she said she had often thought what a beautiful world this would be, when we should see every thing right side up. Now, we see every thing topsy-turvy, and all is confusion. For a person who knows nothing of this fact in the science of optics, this seemed quite a remarkable idea.

Practice your own illuminated letter here.

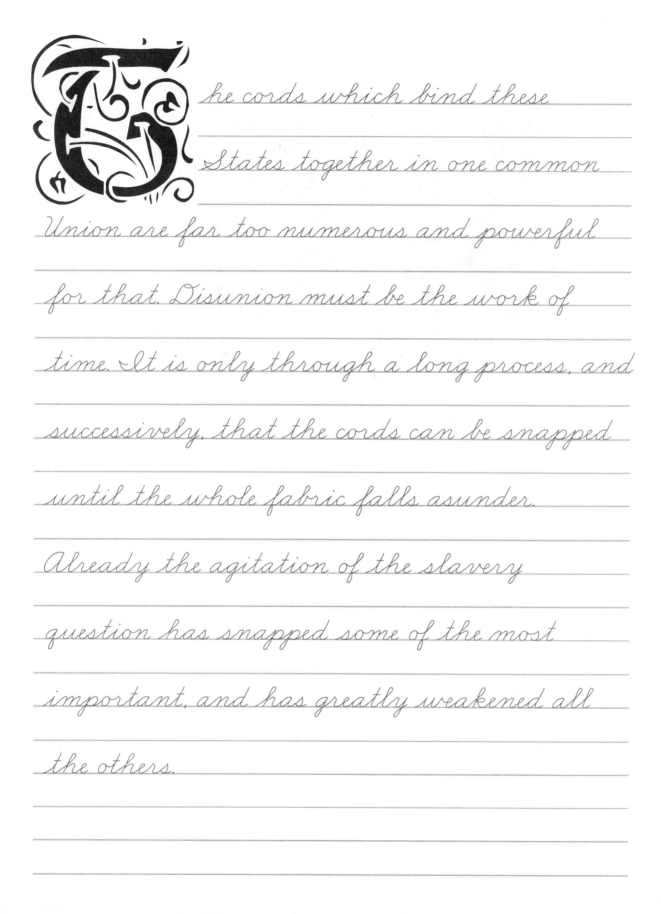

The cords which bind these States together in one common Union are far too numerous and powerful for that. Disunion must be the work of time. It is only through a long process, and successively, that the cords can be snapped until the whole fabric falls asunder. Already the agitation of the slavery question has snapped some of the most important, and has greatly weakened all the others.

Practice your own illuminated letter here.

It may, indeed, keep them connected; but the connection will partake much more of the character of subjugation on the part of the weaker to the stronger than the union of free, independent, and sovereign States in one confederation, as they stood in the early stages of the government, and which only is worthy of the sacred name of Union.

Practice your own illuminated letter here.

The question is simply this:
Can a Negro, whose ancestors
were imported into this country, and sold
as slaves, become a member of the political
community formed and brought into
existence by the Constitution of the United
States, and as such become entitled to all
the rights, and privileges, and immunities,
guarantied by that instrument to the
citizen?

Practice your own illuminated letter here.

"A house divided against itself

cannot stand." I believe this

government cannot endure permanently

half slave and half free. I do not expect the

Union to be dissolved—I do not expect the

house to fall—but I do expect it will cease

to be divided. It will become all one thing.

or all the other.

Practice your own illuminated letter here.

ither the opponents of slavery will arrest the further spread of it, and place it where the public mind shall rest in the belief that it is in the course of ultimate extinction; or its advocates will push it forward, till it shall become alike lawful in all the States, old as well as new—North as well as South.

Practice your own illuminated letter here.

Our present condition, achieved in a manner unprecedented in the history of nations, illustrates the American idea that governments rest upon the consent of the governed, and that it is the right of the people to alter or abolish governments whenever they become destructive of the ends for which they were established.

Practice your own illuminated letter here.

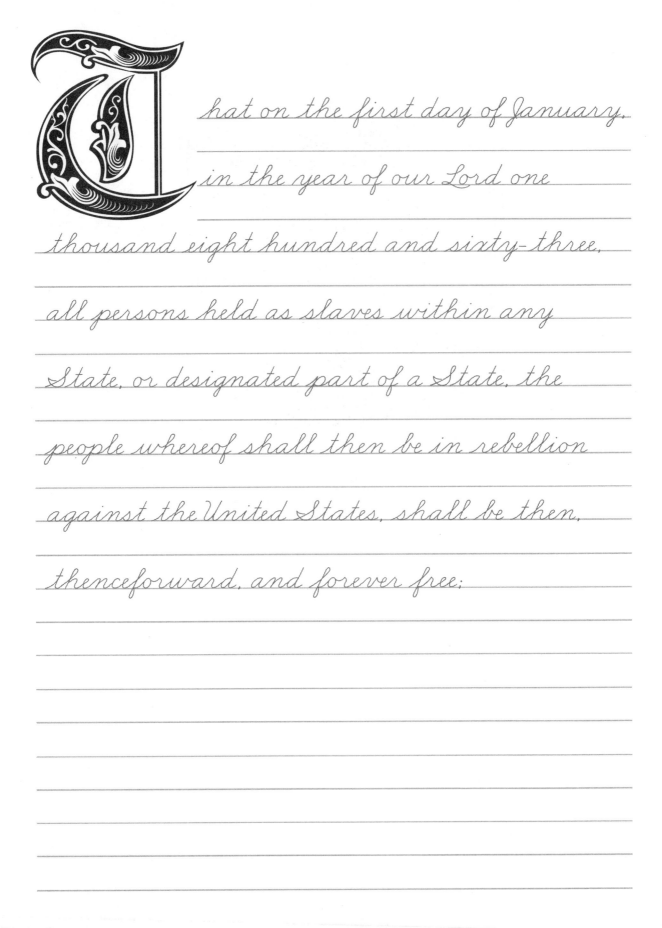

That on the first day of January,
in the year of our Lord one
thousand eight hundred and sixty-three,
all persons held as slaves within any
State, or designated part of a State, the
people whereof shall then be in rebellion
against the United States, shall be then,
thenceforward, and forever free:

Practice your own illuminated letter here.

And the Executive Government of the United States, including the military and naval authority thereof, will recognize and maintain the freedom of such persons and will do no act or acts to repress such persons, or any of them, in any efforts they may make for their actual freedom.

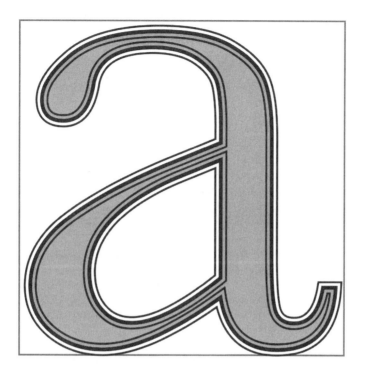

Practice your own illuminated letter here.

Four score and seven years ago our fathers brought forth on this continent, a new nation, conceived in Liberty, and dedicated to the proposition that all men are created equal. Now we are engaged in a great civil war, testing whether that nation, or any nation so conceived and so dedicated, can long endure.

Practice your own illuminated letter here.

e are met on a great battle-field of that war. We have come to dedicate a portion of that field, as a final resting place for those who here gave their lives that that nation might live. It is altogether fitting and proper that we should do this.

Practice your own illuminated letter here.

To those of my race who depend

on bettering their condition in

a foreign land or who underestimate the

importance of cultivating friendly relations

with the Southern white man, who is their

next-door neighbor, I would say: "Cast down

your bucket where you are"—cast it down

in making friends in every manly way

of the people of all races by whom we are

surrounded.

Practice your own illuminated letter here.

No race can prosper till it learns that there is as much dignity in tilling a field as in writing a poem. It is at the bottom of life we must begin, and not at the top. Nor should we permit our grievances to overshadow our opportunities.

Practice your own illuminated letter here.

Legislation is powerless to eradicate racial instincts or to abolish distinctions based upon physical differences, and the attempt to do so can only result in accentuating the difficulties of the present situation. If the civil and political rights of both races be equal, one cannot be inferior to the other civilly or politically. If one race be inferior to the other socially, the Constitution of the United States cannot put them upon the same plane.

Practice your own illuminated letter here.

In "Pilgrim's Progress" the Man with the Muck-rake is set forth as the example of him whose vision is fixed on carnal instead of on spiritual things. Yet he also typifies the man who in this life consistently refuses to see aught that is lofty, and fixes his eyes with solemn intentness only on that which is vile and debasing.

Practice your own illuminated letter here.

The men with the muck-rakes are often indispensable to the well-being of society; but only if they know when to stop raking the muck, and to look upward to the celestial crown above them, to the crown of worthy endeavor.

Practice your own illuminated letter here.

eutrality is no longer feasible or desirable where the peace of the world is involved and the freedom of its peoples. and the menace to that peace and freedom lies in the existence of autocratic governments backed by organized force which is controlled wholly by their will. not by the will of their people.

Practice your own illuminated letter here.

We have seen the last of neutrality in such circumstances. We are at the beginning of an age in which it will be insisted that the same standards of conduct and of responsibility for wrong done shall be observed among nations and their governments that are observed among the individual citizens of civilized states.

Practice your own illuminated letter here.

The United States is the world's best hope, but if you fetter her in the interests and quarrels of other nations, if you tangle her in the intrigues of Europe, you will destroy her power for good and endanger her very existence. Leave her to march freely through the centuries to come as in the years that have gone.

Practice your own illuminated letter here.

Strong, generous, and confident, she has nobly served mankind. Beware how you trifle with your marvelous inheritance, this great land of ordered liberty, for if we stumble and fall, freedom and civilization everywhere will go down in ruin.

Practice your own illuminated letter here.

Yesterday, December 7, 1941—a date which will live in infamy—the United States of America was suddenly and deliberately attacked by naval and air forces of the Empire of Japan.

Practice your own illuminated letter here.

ut always will our whole

nation remember the character

of the onslaught against us. No matter

how long it may take us to overcome

this premeditated invasion, the American

people in their righteous might will win

through to absolute victory. I believe that

I interpret the will of the Congress and of

the people when I assert that we will not

only defend ourselves to the uttermost, but

will make it very certain that this form of

treachery shall never again endanger us.

Practice your own illuminated letter here.

It is logical that the United States should do whatever it is able to do to assist in the return of normal economic health in the world, without which there can be no political stability and no assured peace. Our policy is directed not against any country or doctrine but against hunger, poverty, desperation, and chaos. Its purpose should be the revival of working economy in the world so as to permit the emergence of political and social conditions in which free institutions can exist.

Practice your own illuminated letter here.

It would be neither fitting nor efficacious for this Government to undertake to draw up unilaterally a program designed to place Europe on its feet economically. This is the business of the Europeans. The initiative, I think, must come from Europe. The role of this country should consist of friendly aid in the drafting of a European program so far as it may be practical for us to do so.

Practice your own illuminated letter here.

Sometimes the processes of democracy are slow, and I have known some of our leaders to say that a benevolent dictatorship would accomplish the ends desired in a much shorter time than it takes to go through the democratic processes of discussion and the slow formation of public opinion.

Practice your own illuminated letter here.

But there is no way of insuring that a dictatorship will remain benevolent or that power once in the hands of a few will be returned to the people without struggle or revolution. This we have learned by experience and we accept the slow processes of democracy because we know that short-cuts compromise principles on which no compromise is possible.

Practice your own illuminated letter here.

Five years after a world war has been won, men's hearts should anticipate a long peace—and men's minds should be free from the heavy weight that comes with war. But this is not such a period—for this is not a period of peace. This is a time of "the cold war." This is a time when all the world is split into two vast, increasingly hostile armed camps—a time of a great armament race.

Practice your own illuminated letter here.

Those of us who shout the loudest about Americanism in making character assassinations are all too frequently those who, by our own words and acts, ignore some of the basic principles of Americanism: The right to criticize; The right to hold unpopular beliefs; The right to protest; The right of independent thought. The exercise of these rights should not cost one single American citizen his reputation or his right to a livelihood.

Practice your own illuminated letter here.

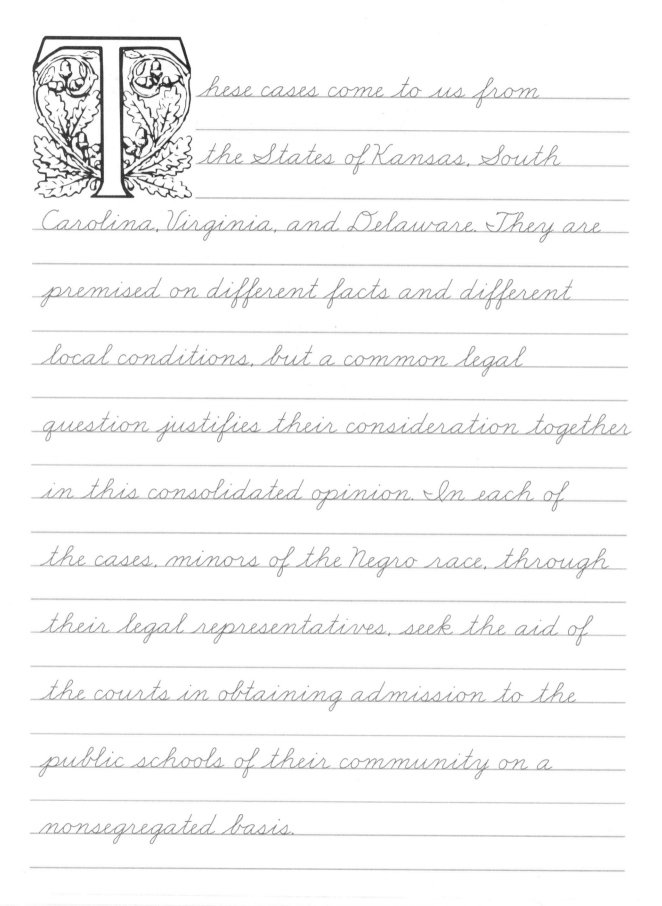

These cases come to us from the States of Kansas, South Carolina, Virginia, and Delaware. They are premised on different facts and different local conditions, but a common legal question justifies their consideration together in this consolidated opinion. In each of the cases, minors of the Negro race, through their legal representatives, seek the aid of the courts in obtaining admission to the public schools of their community on a nonsegregated basis.

Practice your own illuminated letter here.

We conclude that, in the field of public education, the doctrine of "separate but equal" has no place. Separate educational facilities are inherently unequal. Therefore, we hold that the plaintiffs and others similarly situated for whom the actions have been brought are, by reason of the segregation complained of, deprived of the equal protection of the laws guaranteed by the Fourteenth Amendment.

Practice your own illuminated letter here.

And so, my fellow Americans: ask not what your country can do for you—ask what you can do for your country. My fellow citizens of the world: ask not what America will do for you, but what together we can do for the freedom of man. Finally, whether you are citizens of America or citizens of the world, ask of us here the same high standards of strength and sacrifice which we ask of you.

Practice your own illuminated letter here.

With a good conscience our only sure reward, with history the final judge of our deeds, let us go forth to lead the land we love, asking His blessing and His help, but knowing that here on earth God's work must truly be our own.

Practice your own illuminated letter here.

Putting America back to work means putting all Americans back to work. Ending inflation means freeing all Americans from the terror of runaway living costs. All must share in the productive work of this "new beginning" and all must share in the bounty of a revived economy. With the idealism and fair play which are the core of our system and our strength, we can have a strong and prosperous America at peace with itself and the world.

Practice your own illuminated letter here.

t is time for us to realize that we are too great a nation to limit ourselves to small dreams. We are not, as some would have us believe, doomed to an inevitable decline. I do not believe in a fate that will fall on us no matter what we do. I do believe in a fate that will fall on us if we do nothing.

Practice your own illuminated letter here.

So, with all the creative energy at our command, let us begin an era of national renewal. Let us renew our determination, our courage, and our strength. And let us renew our faith and our hope.

Practice your own illuminated letter here.

There is one sign the Soviets can make that would be unmistakable, that would advance dramatically the cause of freedom and peace. General Secretary Gorbachev, if you seek peace, if you seek prosperity for the Soviet Union and Eastern Europe, if you seek liberalization: Come here to this gate! Mr. Gorbachev, open this gate! Mr. Gorbachev, tear down this wall!

Practice your own illuminated letter here.

FREE DRAWING

Additional products from

MultiMedia

Classical Christian Education...
Made Approachable

As a modern parent, are you intimidated at the prospect of building a classical, Christian education for your family? Let this booklet show you a blueprint for the tools of learning! Learn how you too can build your family's home-centered, classical education using the building blocks of knowledge, understanding, and wisdom.

Classical Acts & Facts History Cards

Classical Conversations has developed its own timeline of 161 historical events, representing major cultures on every continent. The events are divided into seven ages and produced as cards similar to our Classical Acts & Facts Science Cards, with the event title on the front and a fuller description of the event on the back. Each card front also contains a beautiful memory peg image. Images were chosen to serve families all the way through cultural studies in the upper levels of Challenge. The back of each card also includes a world map, pinpointing the event location, and a general timeline, illustrating when the event occurred relative to known history.